The Golden Age of Jazz

The definitive anthology of jazz songs from the Twenties to the Fifties.

The Golden Age of Jazz

The definitive anthology of jazz songs from the Twenties to the Fifties.

Wise Publications
London/New York/Paris/Sydney/Copenhagen/Madrid/Tokyo

Music Sales Limited
8/9 Frith Street,
London W1D 3JB, England.
Music Sales Pty Limited
120 Rothschild Avenue,
Rosebery, NSW 2018, Australia.

Order No. AM957242
ISBN 0-7119-7333-4
This book © Copyright 1996 & 2000
by Wise Publications
Previously published as Jazz Decades The Twenties (AM92389),
The Thirties (AM92390), The Forties (AM92391) and The Fifties (AM92392)

Compiled by Peter Evans and Peter Lavender
Printed and bound in Malta by Interprint Ltd

Your Guarantee of Quality

As publishers, we strive to produce every book
to the highest commercial standards. This music book
has been carefully designed to minimise awkward page
turns and to make playing from it a real pleasure.
Throughout, the printing and binding have been planned
to ensure a sturdy, attractive publication which should
give years of enjoyment. If your copy fails to meet our
high standards, please inform us and we will gladly replace it.

www.musicsales.com

Music Sales' complete catalogue describes thousands of titles
and is available in full colour sections by subject, direct from
Music Sales Limited. Please state your areas of interest
and send a cheque/postal order for £1.50 for postage to:
Music Sales Limited, Newmarket Road,
Bury St. Edmunds, Suffolk IP33 3YB.

The Twenties

That's A Plenty

Words by Ray Gilbert. Music by Lew Pollack

That's a plen - ty's, got - ta beat _ in it, The rhy - thms got a lot of heat _ in it,
Dix - ie - land comes ooz - in' out _ of it, The Dix - ie - land - ers sure are proud _ of it, They

Bet - cha five, _ ten to five, _ it's gon-na get-cha do-in' what it's do-in' to me. _ The
call it jazz, _ what it has, _

That's a plen - ty for me. ____ It takes you down to New Or - leans _ down

Fascinating Rhythm

By George Gershwin & Ira Gershwin

Baby Face

Words & Music by Harry Akst & Benny Davis

Ros - y cheeks and turn'd up nose and curl - y hair, _____ I'm rav - ing
'bout my ba - by now, _____ Pret - ty lit - tle dim - ples here and
dim - ples there; _____ Don't want to live with - out her, I love her good - ness

knows, I wrote a song a - bout her And here's the way it goes:

CHORUS

Ba - by Face, ___ You've got the cut - est lit - tle

Ba - by Face, ___ There's not an - oth - er one could take your place. ___

Ba - by Face, ___ my poor heart ___ is jump - in',

You sure have start-ed some-thin', Ba - by Face; I'm up in heav-en when I'm in your fond em - brace, I did-n't need a shove 'Cause I just fell in love with your pret - ty Ba - by Face. Face.

Can't Help Lovin' Dat Man

Music by Jerome Kern. Words by Oscar Hammerstein II

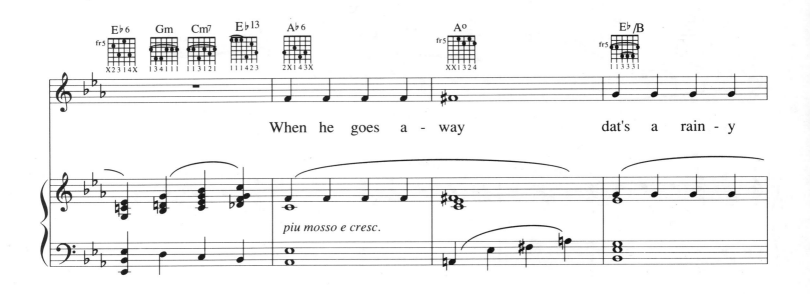

When he goes a - way dat's a rain - y

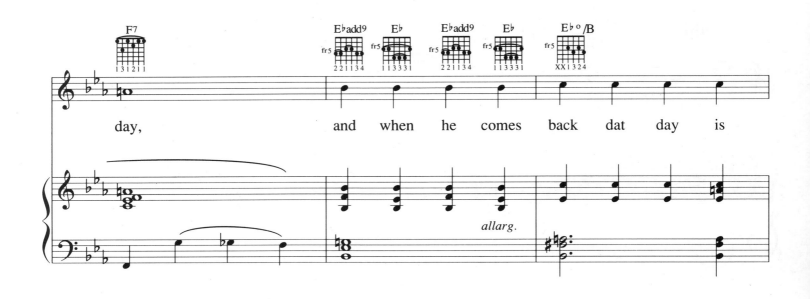

day, and when he comes back dat day is

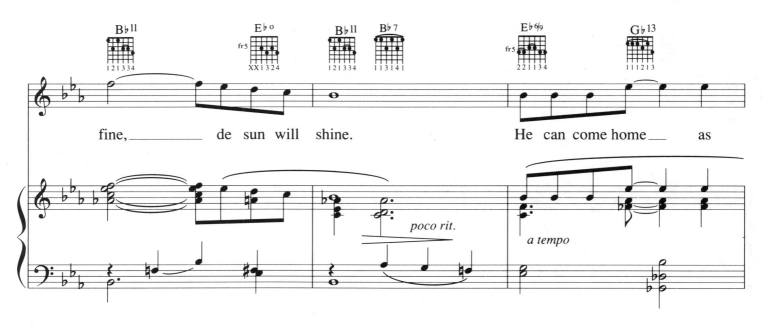

fine,_____ de sun will shine. He can come home_____ as

Blues My Naughty Sweetie Gives To Me

Words & Music by Arthur N. Swanstrom, Charles R. McGarron & Carey Morgan

Baby Won't You Please Come Home

Words & Music by Charles Warfield & Clarence Williams

28

Hard Hearted Hannah

Words & Music by Jack Yellen, Milton Ager, Bob Bigelow & Charles Bates

In old Sa-van-nah, I said, Sa-van-nah, The weath-er there is nice and warm;

The cli-mate's of the south-ern brand,— But here's what I don't un-der-stand;—

They've got a gal there, A pret-ty gal there, Who's cold-er than an arc-tic storm;— Got a

31

Five Foot Two, Eyes Of Blue

Words by Sam Lewis & Joe Young. Music by Ray Henderson

Hey Lawdy Mama

Words & Music by Cleve Reed

got a mouth full of gold _____

_____ Ev - 'ry time he kiss ___ me, makes my blood ___ go

1 - 5.

cold. _____ Now the

6.

door. _____

HEY LAWDY MAMA (additional verses):

VERSE 2:
Now the man I love, the man I long to see
Hey Lawdy Mama, little pretty Mama
The man I love, the man I long to see
He's in Cincinatti and he won't write to me.

VERSE 3:
Now the man I love got his feet right on the ground
Hey Lawdy Mama, little pretty Mama
The man I love got his feet right on the ground
He's tailor made, he ain't no hand me down.

VERSE 4:
I'm down and out, ain't got a friend in the world
Hey Lawdy Mama, hey pretty Mama
I'm down and out, ain't got a friend in the world
I know I've been a fool for being someone else's girl.

VERSE 5:
When I had money, I had money to spend
Hey Lawdy Mama, little pretty Mama
When I had money, I had money to spend
Every time I left home, I had a brand new friend.

VERSE 6:
Soon this morning, about a quarter to four
Hey Lawdy Mama, little pretty Mama
Soon this morning, about a quarter to four
You brought your new girl right up to my door.

I Ain't Got Nobody
(And There's Nobody Cares For Me)

Words & Music by Roger Graham & Spencer Williams

1. There's a say-ing go-ing 'round, and I be-gin to think it's true. It's
2. Wish I on-ly had some-one that I could real-ly call my own. For

aw-ful hard to love some-one when they don't care 'bout you.
I would mar-ry him at once, and take him to my home;

Once I had a lov-in' man, as good as an-y in this town, But
Ev-'ry night I sigh and cry, no hap-pi-ness at all I find, I

CHORUS

now I'm sad and lone - ly, for he's gone and turned me down.____ 'Cause
have no one to love me, no one to con - tent my mind.____

I_____ ain't got no - bo - dy, And there's

no - bo - dy cares for me._____ I'm____

so sad and lone - ly, won't some-bo-dy come and take a chance with

Honeysuckle Rose

Music by Thomas 'Fats' Waller. Words by Andy Razaf

Have no use for oth-er sweets of an-y kind, since the day you came a-round. From the start, I in-stant-ly made up my mind,

43

King Porter Stomp

By Ferdinand 'Jelly Roll' Morton

Medium ragtime with swing feeling

Interlude

Mama Don't Allow It

Words & Music by Chas 'Cow Cow' Davenport

You've heard of the wo-man who liv'd in a shoe, What a

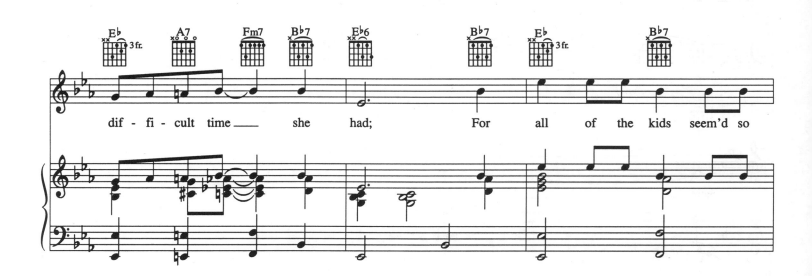

dif-fi-cult time ___ she had; For all of the kids seem'd so

anx - ious to do, All the things that would make her mad. A

vis - i - tor called on them one day, And here's what he heard all the

lit - tle kids say: 1. Ma - ma don't al - low no mu - sic played in

here, _____ Ma - ma don't al - low no

Chorus

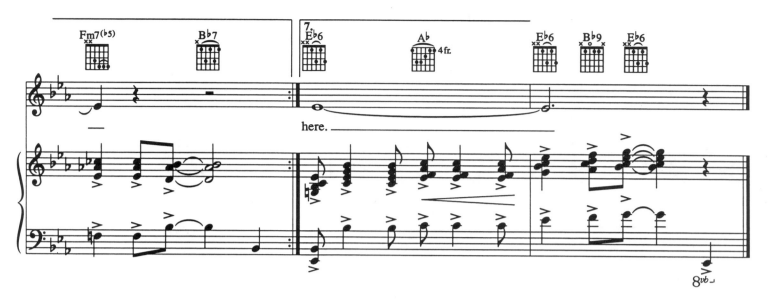

Verse 2:

Mama don't allow no piano play'n here,
Mama don't allow no piano play'n here;
Tho' you were of Paderewski fame,
She still would put you in the "Hall of Shame",
'Cause mama don't allow no piano play'n in here.

Verse 3:

Mama don't allow no slap-bass playr's in here,
Mama don't allow no slap-bass playr's in here;
My mam claims it really is a sin,
To play upon a swollen violin;
So mama don't allow no slap-bass playr's in here.

Verse 4:

Mama don't allow no drummer man in here,
Mama don't allow no drummer man in here;
Mama says you're gonna go "boom",
If she should catch you drummin' in this room;
'Cause mama don't allow no drummer man in here.

Verse 5:

Mama don't allow no saxophones in here,
Mama don't allow no saxophones in here;
Ev'ry time she listens to a sax,
She feels so good, she pays her income tax;
So mama don't allow no saxophones in here.

Verse 6:

Mama don't allow no truckin' done in here,
Mama don't allow no truckin' done in here;
After mama switches out the light,
I like to do my truckin' ev'ry night;
But mama don't allow no truckin' done in here.

Verse 7:

Mama don't allow no nothin' done in here,
Mama don't allow no nothin' done in here;
Don't know how I'll ever get along,
'Cause when I'm doin' nothin', somethin's wrong;
But mama don't allow no nothin' done in here.

Hear Me Talkin' To Ya

Words & Music by Louis Armstrong

get his pants. — } Ah, you hear me talk - in' to ya.   Don't bite my
his or mine. __ }

tongue.   You want to be my { man __ } you got to
                                                  { wom-an }

fetch it with you when you come. ___

Please Help Me Get Him Off My Mind

Words & Music by Bessie Smith

weigh two hun - dred now I'm down _____ to skin and bones.

1. It's all _____ a - bout a man ___ who al - ways
2.-4. *(See additional lyrics)*

kicked and dogged me 'round. _ It's all _

___ a - bout a man ___ who al - ways ___ kicked and dogged me 'round; _

Additional Lyrics

2. I've come to see you gypsy, beggin' on my bended knees,
   I've come to see you gypsy, beggin' on my bended knees,
   That man's put something on me, oh take it off of me, please.

3. It starts at my forehead and goes clean down to my toes.
   It starts at my forehead and goes clean down to my toes.
   Oh, how I'm sufferin' gypsy, nobody but the good Lawd knows.

4. Gypsy, don't hurt him, fix him for me one more time,
   Oh, don't hurt him gypsy, fix him for me one more time.
   Just make him love me, but, please mam, take him off my mind.

Memphis Blues

Words & Music by W.C. Handy

Moderate blues tempo

1. Hon - ey I've ___ been down, down to Mem - phis town, Where the peo - ple smile
2. Oh, that mel - o - dy sure ap - peals ___ to me, Like a moun - tain stream,

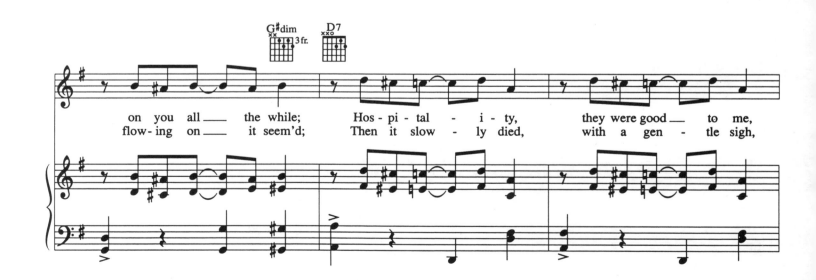

on you all ___ the while; Hos - pi - tal - i - ty, they were good ___ to me,
flow - ing on ___ it seem'd; Then it slow - ly died, with a gen - tle sigh,

Could-n't spend a dime, had the grand - est time, I went out a-danc - in' with a
As the breeze that whines in the sum - mer pines, Hear me peo - ple, hear me peo - ple,

Ten - nes-see dear, A fel - low there nam'd Han - dy had a band you should hear,
hear me, I pray, I'll take a mil - lion les - sons till I learn how to play,

While they gen - tly swayed, all them dark - ies played real har - mon -
Seems I hear it yet, sim - ply can't for - get, that blue re -

- y. I nev - er will for - get the tune that Han - dy called the Mem - phis
-frain. There's no - thing like the Han - dy band that plays the Mem - phis blues so

Slow chorus

blues, _____ Oh, them blues. _____ They got a fid - dle there that al - ways
grand, _____ Oh, them blues. _____

slick - ens his hair. _____ Oh, Lord - y, how _____ he pulls on his bow. _____ And when you

hear that tune, _____ Lis - ten to the trom - bones croon, _____ They

moan just like _____ a sin - ner on re - viv - al day, On that old re - viv - al

day. _____ That mel - an - cho - ly strain, that ev - er haunt - ing re - frain ___ is like a

dar - key moan - in' a song, _____ Here comes the ve - ry part ___ that

wraps a spell a - round my heart, _____ It sets me wild ___ to

hear that love - ly tune a - gain - Those Mem - phis blues. ___ They got a ___

Mississippi Mud

Words & Music by Harry Barris

Moderately slow, with a beat

When the sun goes down, the tide goes out The peo-ple gath-er 'round and they all be-gin to shout "Hey! Hey! Un-cle Dud__ it's a treat to beat your feet on the Mis-sis-sip-pi Mud It's a treat to beat your feet on the

Sweet Sue - Just You

Words by Will J. Harris. Music by Victor Young

68

No-one else it seems_____ ev - er shares my dreams _____ And with -

out you, dear, I don't know what I'd do, _____ In this heart of mine _____

_____ you live all the time _____ Sweet Sue, _____ Just

You. _____ Ev - 'ry You. _____

poco rit.

Royal Garden Blues

By Clarence Williams & Spencer Williams

Here's why I'm ra-vin'___ here's why I'm ra-vin' If it's blues you are cra-vin' just come on down_

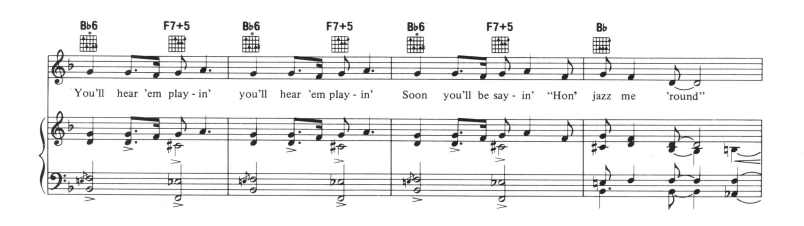

You'll hear 'em play-in' you'll hear 'em play-in' Soon you'll be say-in' "Hon' jazz me 'round"

Be - cause your feet they can't re - fuse___

What's that fa-mil-liar strain that true blue note re-frain It's driv-in' me in-sane

Way Down Yonder In New Orleans

Words & Music by Henry Creamer & Turner Layton

Sorrowful Blues

Words & Music by Bessie Smith

Additional Lyrics

2. I got nineteen men and won't want more;
   I got nineteen men and won't want more.
   If I had one more I'd let that nineteen go.

3. I'm gonna tell you, Daddy, like Solomon told the Jew;
   I'm gonna tell you, Daddy, like Solomon told the Jew.
   If you don't likee me, I sure don't likee you.

4. It's hard to love another woman's man;
   It's hard to love another woman's man.
   You can't catch him when you want him, you got to
      catch him when you can.

5. Have you ever seen a preacher throw a sweet potato pie?
   Have you ever seen a preacher throw a sweet potato pie?
   Just step in my backyard and taste a piece of mine.

Crazy Blues

Words & Music by Perry Bradford

He's / She's leav-in' all the time. _____

Now I see ___ my poor love ___ was blind. _____

___ Now I got the cra - zy blues since ___

___ my ba - by went a - way. I ain't got no time to

The Thirties

Caravan

By Duke Ellington, Irving Mills & Juan Tizol

Moderately, quasi misterioso

you _____ Be - side me here be - neath the

blue _____ My dream of love is com - ing true _____

_____ With - in our des - ert car - a - van. _____

Drop Me Off In Harlem

Words by Nick Kenny Music by Duke Ellington

Heav-en up in Har-lem.___ I don't want___ your Dix - ie,___

you can keep___ your Dix - ie,_____ There's no one down in

Dix - ie who can take me 'way from my own Har - lem,_____

Har-lem has___ those south-ern skies,___ they're in my ba-by's smile,___ I

i-dol-ize___ my ba-by's eyes___ and class-y up-town style. If

Har-lem moved___ to Chi-na,___ I know of no-thing fi-

-ner,___ Than to stow a-way___ on a 'plane some day and have them

drop me off in Har-lem.___ Har-lem.

Don't Worry 'Bout Me

Words by Ted Koehler. Music by Rube Bloom

East Of The Sun
(And West Of The Moon)

Words & Music by Brooks Bowman

Slowly, With Expression

East Of The Sun and west of the moon, We'll build a dream-house of love, dear. Near to the sun in the day, Near to the moon at night, We'll live in a love-ly

How Ya Baby

Words by J C Johnson. Music by Thomas Waller

Georgia On My Mind

Words by Stuart Gorrell. Music by Hoagy Carmichael

In A Sentimental Mood

Words & Music by Duke Ellington, Irving Mills & Manny Kurtz

In a sen-ti-men-tal mood_____ I can see the stars come through my room_____

_____ While your lov-ing at-ti-tude_____ is like a flame that lights the

gloom. On the wings of ev-'ry kiss,_____ drifts a mel-o-dy so strange and sweet;

_____ In this sen-ti-men-tal bliss_____ you make my par - a - dise com -

plete. Rose pet-als seem to fall, it's all like a dream to call you

mine. My heart's a light-er thing since

106

I'm Gettin' Sentimental Over You

Words by Ned Washington. Music by Geo. Bassman

Nev - er thought I'd fall, _____ but now I hear love call, _____ I'm

get - tin' sen - ti - ment - al o - ver you.

Things you say and do, _____ just thrill me through and through, _____ I'm

get - tin' sen - ti - ment - al o - ver you. I thought I was hap - py, I could

In The Mood

Words by Andy Razaf. Music by Joe Garland

A7   E7

Hope she tells me may-be, what a wing it will be.___ So I said, po-lite-ly, "Dar-lin'
there's a mess of moon-light, won't-cha share it with me?!" "Well" she an-swered, "Mis-ter don't-cha

Bm7   A6   D6   F7 E9 A6

may I in-trude? She said,___ "Don't keep me wait-in' when I'm in the mood."
know that it's rude___ to keep___ my two lips wait-in' when they're in the mood?!"

A6   C°7 Bm7   E11 E7-9   A6   C°7 Bm7

In the mood,___ that's what she told me. In the mood,___

E11 E7-9   A6   C°7 Bm7   E11

and when she told me in the mood,___ my heart was skip-pin'. It

It Don't Mean A Thing
(If It Ain't Got That Swing)

Words by Irving Mills. Music by Duke Ellington

give that rhy-thm ev'-ry-thing you got.

Oh, it don't mean a thing if it ain't got that swing, —

(doo wah, — doo wah, doo wah, doo wah, doo wah, —

— doo wah, doo wah, doo wah.) It wah.)

Let's Dance

Words & Music by Fanny Baldridge, Gregory Stone & Joseph Bonime

Just For A Thrill

Words & Music by Lil Armstrong & Don Raye

I held your heart _____ for just a day __ but when you
Al- though you're free _____ and just hav- ing fun __ to me you're

laughed _____ and snatched it a- way __ you made my
still _____ the on- ly one __ you made my

heart stand still _____ just for a thrill.
heart stand still _____ just for a

just for a thrill. _____

rit.

123

Moonglow

Words & Music by Will Hudson, Eddie de Lange & Irving Mills

Solitude

Words by Eddie de Lange & Irving Mills. Music by Duke Ellington

Pick Yourself Up

Music by Jerome Kern. Words by Dorothy Fields

Noth - ing's im-poss-i-ble I have found, for when my chin is

on the ground, I pick my-self up, dust my-self off, start all o-ver a-

-gain.   Don't   lose your con - fi - dence   if   you   slip,   be

grate - ful   for   a   pleas - ant   trip,   and   pick your-self   up,   dust your-self   off,

start   all   o - ver   a - gain.   Work   like   a   soul   in -

-spir - ed,   till the   bat-tle of the day   is   won.   You   may be sick   and

tir - ed,   but you'll be   a   man   my   son!   Will   you re-mem-ber the

fa - mous men,   who had   to   fall   to rise a - gain?   So take a deep breath,

1.

pick your-self up, start all o-ver a-gain

2.

Pick your-self up,

dust your-self off, start all o-ver a-gain.

Stars Fell On Alabama

Words by Mitchell Parish. Music by Frank Perkins

dra - ma, we kissed in a field of white, and stars fell on Al - a -

ba - ma last night. I can't for-get the

glam - our, your eyes held a ten - der light, and stars fell on Al - a -

ba - ma last night. I nev - er planned in my im - a - gi -

135

Sophisticated Lady

Words by Irving Mills & Mitchell Parish. Music by Duke Ellington

Stormy Weather

Words by Ted Koehler. Music by Harold Arlen

Don't know why_____ there's no sun up in the sky, Storm-y weath-er,____

since my man and I ain't to-geth-er,____ Keeps rain-in' all___ the time,____

All I do is pray___ the Lord a - bove will let me walk in the sun once more. Can't go

on,___ ev - 'ry - thing I had is gone, Storm - y weath - er,___ Since my man and I___ ain't to -

geth - er,___ Keeps rain - in' all___ the time,___ Keeps rain - in' all___ the

1. time.___

Don't know **2.** time.___

Summertime
(from Porgy And Bess)

By George Gershwin, Ira Gershwin, DuBose & Dorothy Heyward

The Joint Is Jumpin'

Words by Andy Razaf & J.C. Johnson. Music by Thomas Waller

The Song Is You

Music by Jerome Kern. Words by Oscar Hammerstein II

Steady 2 beat

I hear mu-sic when I look at you,____

____ a beau-ti-ful theme of ev-'ry dream I ev-er knew,____

hand,_____ a beau-ti-ful mel - o - dy from some en - chant - ed

land,_____ down deep in my heart_____ I hear it

say,_____ is this the day?_____

I a - lone ————

have heard this love - ly strain, ———— I a - lone ————

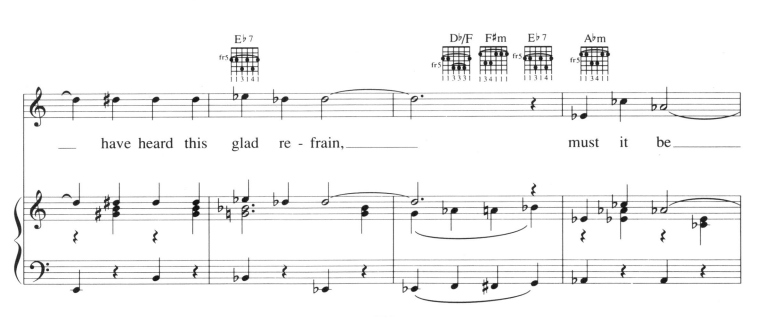

have heard this glad re - frain, ———— must it be ————

for - ev - er in - side of me, _____ why can't I

let it go, _____ why can't I let you know, _____ why can't I

let you know the song my heart would sing, _____ that beau - ti - ful

rhap - so - dy of love and youth and spring,_____ the mu - sic is

sweet,_____ the words are true,_____ the song is

you._____

cresc.

p

The Music Goes Round And Around

Words by Red Hodgson. Music by Edward Farley & Michael Riley

Tuxedo Junction

Words by Buddy Feyne
Music by Erskine Hawkins, William Johnson & Julian Dash

Yesterdays

Music by Jerome Kern. Words by Otto Harbach

The Forties

Across The Alley From The Alamo

Words & Music by Joe Greene

A - cross the al - ley from the Al - a - mo, ___ Lived a

pin - to po - ny and a Na - va - jo, ___

Who sang a sort of In - di - an
Who used to bake fri - jol - es in

Hi - de - ho ___ to the peo - ple pass - ing by. ___
corn - meal dough ___ for the peo - ple pass - ing by. ___

The
They

swish-in' not look-in'_____ Toot! Toot!___ they nev-er came back.___
nev-er heard the whis-tle_____ Toot! Toot!___ they're clear out of sight.___

_____ A - cross the al - ley from the Al - a - mo,___ When the
_____ A - cross the al - ley from the Al - a - mo,___ When the

sum - mer sun de - cides to set - tle low,___ A fly sings an In - di - an
star - light beams it's ten - der, ten - der glow,___ The beams go to sleep and there

Hi - de - ho___ to the peo - ple pass - ing by. ___
ain't no dough ___ for the peo - ple pass - ing by. ___ A - ___

166

Angel Eyes

Words by Earl Brent. Music by Matt Dennis

A Night In Tunisia

Music by Frank Paparelli & John 'Dizzy' Gillespie. Words by Raymond Leveen

A Sunday Kind Of Love

Words & Music by Barbara Belle, Louis Prima, Anita Leonard & Stan Rhodes

Everything But You

By Duke Ellington, Harry James & Don George

Boogie Woogie Bugle Boy

Words & Music by Don Raye & Hughie Prince

But then his num-ber came up, ___ And he was gone with the draft. ___ He's in the ar-my now a-blow-in' re-veil-le, He's the Boo-gie Woo-gie Bu-gle Boy of Com-pa-ny B. ___ They

made him blow a bu-gle for his Un-cle Sam, ___ It
puts the boys to sleep with "boo-gie" ev-'ry night, ___ And

Do Nothin' Till You Hear From Me

Words & Music by Duke Ellington & Bob Russell

188

Harlem Nocturne

Music by Earle Hagen. Words by Dick Rogers

Don't Get Around Much Anymore

Words by Bob Russell. Music by Duke Ellington

193

Drum Boogie

Words & Music by Gene Krupa & Roy Eldridge

Medium – bright

Chorus

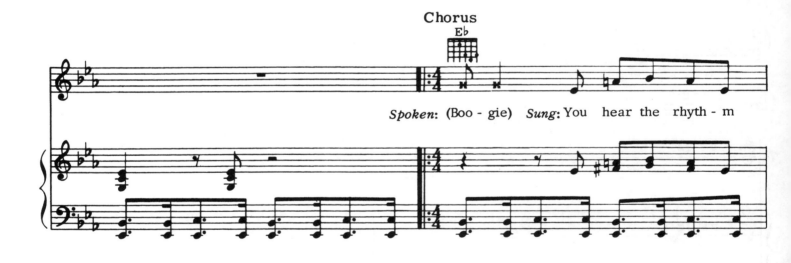

Spoken: (Boo - gie)   *Sung:* You hear the rhyth - m

romp - in',___   (Boo - gie)   You see the drum - mer

God Bless' The Child

Words & Music by Arthur Herzog Jr. & Billie Holiday

I'm Beginning To See The Light

Words & Music by Harry James, Duke Ellington, Johnny Hodges & Don George

Intermission Riff

Words by Steve Graham. Music by Ray Wetzel

I'll Remember April

Words & Music by Don Raye, Gene de Paul & Patricia Johnson

Opus One

Words & Music by Sy Oliver

Moderate Jump Tempo

I'm wrack-in' my brain, to think of a name, To give to this tune, so Per-ry can croon, And may-be Ol' Bing will give it a fling, And that'll start ev-'ry-one hum-min' the thing. The mel-o-dy's dumb, re-

Perdido

Music by Juan Tizol. Words by Harry Lenk and Ervin Drake

Take The 'A' Train

Words & Music by Billy Strayhorn

To go to Sug-ar Hill 'way up in Har-lem.

If you miss the "A" train,

You'll find you've missed the quick-est way to

Har-lem. Hur-ry, get on now it's

Mad About Him, Sad Without Him,
How Can I Be Glad Without Him Blues

Words & Music by Larry Markes & Dick Charles

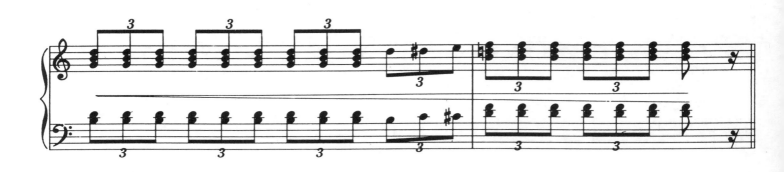

I went to bed last eve - nin' feel - in' blue as I could be____

The Frim Fram Sauce

Words & Music by Joe Ricardel & Redd Evans

Moderate bounce (with a ♪♩ feel)

Violets For Your Furs

Words by Tom Adair. Music by Matt Dennis

furs_____ and gave a lift to the crowds pass-ing by, You smiled at me so sweet-ly, Since then one thought oc- curs, That we fell in love com-plete-ly, The day that you bought me vi-o-lets for my furs. furs.

That Ole Devil Called Love

Words & Music by Doris Fisher & Allan Roberts

He fol-lows me a-round,___ builds me up___ tears me down,___ I

try my best to shake him but he just hangs a-round. It's that

ole Dev-il called love a-gain. Gets be-hind me and keeps giv-ing me that

shove a-gain, Put-ting rain___ in my eyes,

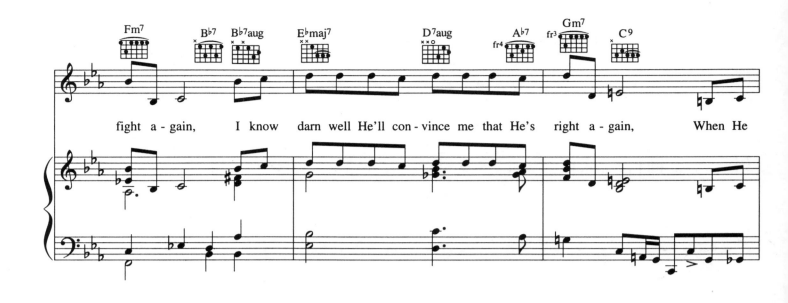

fight a - gain, I know darn well He'll con - vince me that He's right a - gain, When He

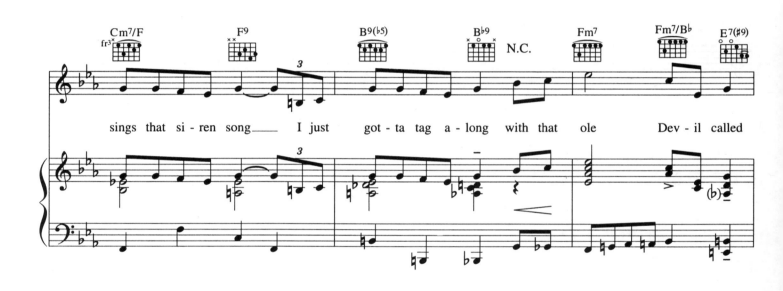

sings that si - ren song___ I just got - ta tag a - long with that ole Dev - il called

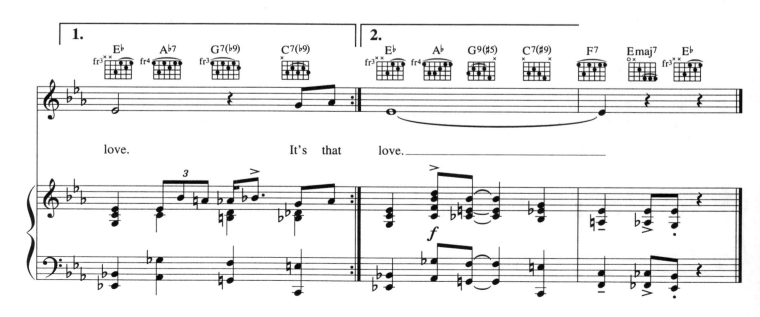

1. love. It's that **2.** love.___

Five Guys Named Moe

Words & Music by Larry Wynn & Jerry Bresler

four eyed___ Moe,_____

no Moe,___

look at bro - ther,_____ look at bro - ther,___

look at bro - ther eat Moe,_____

tell me who the cri-tics all rave a-bout___ five guys named Moe, Ah!

We came out of no-where that don't mean a thing.

We rate high___ and you'll know why___ when you hear us sing,_____

_____ sing, sing, sing, sing._____

High brow, low brow, they all a - gree

we're the best in har - mo - ny____ I'm

tell-ing you folks,_ you real - ly ought to see five guys named Moe.

D.%. al Coda

CODA

sing.____

The Fifties

Alright, Okay, You Win

Words & Music by Sid Wyche & Mayme Watts

Moderately, with rhythm

244

Anthropology

By Dizzy Gillespie & Charlie Parker

Air Conditioned Jungle

By Duke Ellington

Bandstand Boogie

Music by Charles Albertine
Words by Barry Manilow & Bruce Sussman

We're go - in' hop - pin', (Hop!) we're go - in' hop - pin' to - day, where things are
swing - in', (Swing!) we're gon - na swing in the crowd, and we'll be

pop - pin' (Pop!) the Phil - a - del - phi - a way; we're gon - na drop in (Drop!) on all the
cling - in' (Cling!) and float - in' high on a cloud, the phones are ring - in' (Ring!) my mom and

Hey!__ It's Mis - ter Dick Clark; what a place you've got here,

swell spot, the mu - sic's hot here. Best in the East, give it

at least a sev - en - ty - five! Now for

Band - stand. __

Stroll on A-mer-i-can, Lin-dy Hop and Slop, it's A-mer-i-can

Eb9 D7+5 Db13 C7 Bmaj7

tune in, I'm on, turn on, I'm in, I'm on!

Bb6 Eb9 Eb/F

To - day,

C7 Bmaj7 Bb6

Band - stand.

258

Black Coffee

Words & Music by Paul Francis Webster & Sonny Burke

Bark For Barksdale

By Gerry Mulligan

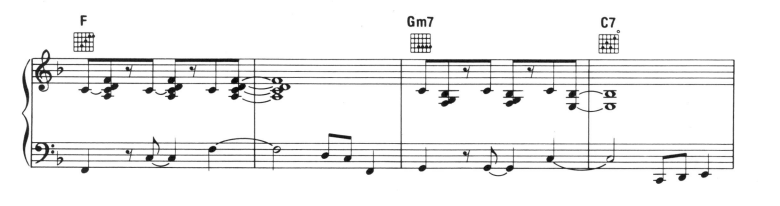

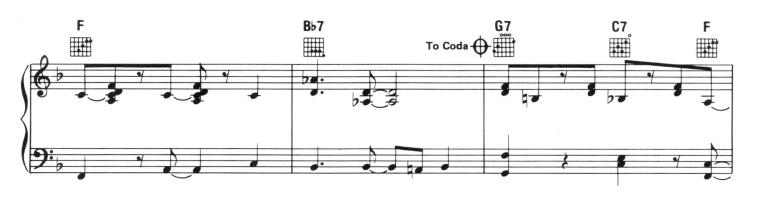

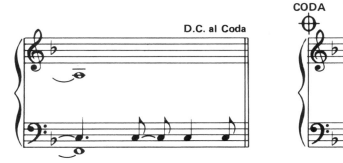

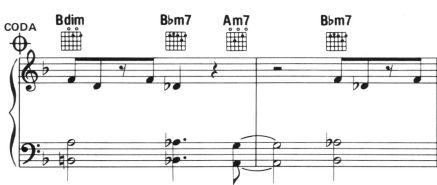

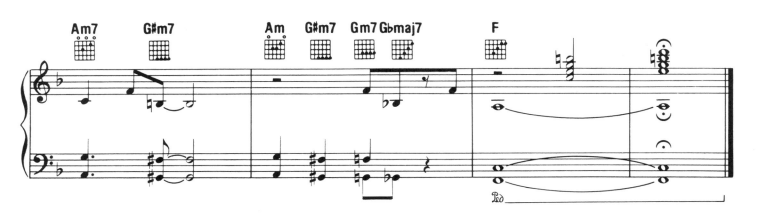

Bernie's Tune

By Bernie Miller

Cute

Words by Stanley Styne. Music by Neal Hefti

Desafinado
(Slightly Out Of Tune)

English Lyric by Jon Hendricks & Jessie Cavanaugh
Music by Antonio Carlos Jobim

Don't Dream Of Anybody But Me
(Li'l Darlin')

Words by Bart Howard. Music by Neal Hefti

1. You may va - ca - tion in Ha - wa - ii
2. Tho' you may fly to Scot - tish High - lands
3. No mat - ter where you care to tra - vel

Or go to Swit - zer - land to ski. When you're
Or try some isle near Nap - o - li. When you're
No mat - ter who you choose to see. When-

scan - ning the snow - cov - ered moun - tains Or fan - ning your - self by the sea,
whist - lin' "The Camp-bells are com - ing," Or hum - ming "The Isle of Ca - pri,"
ev - er your head hits that pil - low What - ev - er the hour may be,

When you vis - it a night club in 'Fris - co,
When a guy with a "mike" in a night club

And the sing - er keeps sing - in' off
be - gins bel - low - ing some - thin' off

key
key

Won't ev - en mind if sud - den - ly she re -
(he)

minds you of me!

an - y - bo - dy but me!

Don't dream of an - y - bo - dy but me!

Fly Me To The Moon
(In Other Words)

Words & Music by Bart Howard

Fever

Words & Music by John Davenport & Eddie Cooley

you all know. Fe-ver is-n't such a new thing,

fe-ver start-ed long a go. burn.

Verse 3 Romeo loved Juliet,
         Juliet she felt the same,
         When he put his arms around her, he said,
         "Julie, baby you're my flame."

Chorus Thou givest fever, when we kisseth
        Fever with thy flaming youth,
        Fever - I'm afire
        Fever, yea I burn forsooth.

Verse 4 Captain Smith and Pocahontas
         Had a very mad affair,
         When her Daddy tried to kill him, she said,
         "Daddy-o don't you dare."

Chorus Give me fever, with his kisses,
        Fever when he holds me tight.
        Fever - I'm his Missus
        Oh Daddy won't you treat him right.

Verse 5 Now you've listened to my story
         Here's the point that I have made:
         Chicks were born to give you fever
         Be it fahrenheit or centigrade.

Chorus They give you fever when you kiss them,
        Fever if you live and learn.
        Fever - till you sizzle
        What a lovely way to burn.

Early Autumn

Words by Johnny Mercer

Music by Ralph Burns & Woody Herman

285

Here's That Rainy Day

Words & Music by Johnny Burke & Jimmy Van Heusen

told me a - bout, and I laughed at the thought that it

might turn out this way. _____

Where is that worn out wish that I threw a -

side af - ter it brought my lov - er

Midnight Sun

Words by Johnny Mercer

Music by Sonny Burke & Lionel Hampton

star its own au - ro - ra bo - re - a - lis, sud - den - ly you

held me tight,_____ I could see the mid - night sun._____

_____ I can't ex - plain the sil - ver rain that found me, or was that a

moon - lit veil?_____ The mu - sic of the un - i - verse a -

round me, or was that a night - in - gale? _____ And

then your arms mi - ra - cu - lous - ly found me, sud - den - ly the

sky turned pale, _____ I could see the mid - night sun. _____

Was there such a night, it's a thrill I still don't quite be -

cem-ber, ic - y white and crys - tal - line. _____ But,

oh, my dar - ling al - ways I'll re - mem - ber, when your lips were

close to mine, _____ And {I/we} saw the mid-night sun. __

Your mid - night sun. _____

Lullaby Of Birdland

Music by George Shearing

Words by George David Weiss

in a phrase __ how I feel! __ Have you ev - er heard two

tur - tle doves __ bill and coo __ when they love? __

That's the kind of mag - ic mu - sic we make __ with our lips __

when we kiss! __ And there's a weep-y old wil -

Quiet Village

Music by Leslie Baxter. Words by Mel Leven

Satin Doll

Words by Johnny Mercer

Music by Duke Ellington & Billy Strayhorn

ain't for no girl___ catch-ing me._____ *Spoken: Swich - E -Roo-ney*

Tel - e-phone num - bers   well   you know,   do - ing my rhum - bas

with   u - no,   And   that 'n'   my   sat - in doll.___

The Best Is Yet To Come

Words by Carolyn Leigh. Music by Cy Coleman

Moderately, with a beat

Out of the tree of life___ I just picked me a plum,___

You came a-long and ev - 'ry-thing's start-in' to hum;___

Still it's a real good bet___ The Best Is Yet To Come,___

The Lady Sings The Blues

Words by Billie Holiday. Music by Herbie Nichols

she feels so sad, But now the world will know, she's nev-er gon-na sing them no more.

no more.

The Late Late Show

Words & Music by Roy Alfred & Dave Cavanaugh

Birds that should be dream-ing,

Start in chirp-ing a song; ____ While fire - flies are

gleam-ing, ____ We kissed, kissed all ___ night long. ___

Then we am - ble back to my front door, ___

Witchcraft

Words by Carolyn Leigh. Music by Cy Coleman

Get real...

Play the world's greatest music instantly
with these bumper collections of jazz and blues numbers,
all-time great songs and popular classics.

Easy-to-read melody line arrangements by Jack Long, with chord symbols and lyrics (where appropriate).

The Real Book of **Jazz**

Over 190 great jazz standards including...
A Foggy Day; Ain't Misbehavin'; April In Paris;
Caravan; Crazy Rhythm; Django; Don't Blame Me;
Fascinating Rhythm; Fly Me To The Moon; Frenesi;
Honeysuckle Rose; I'm Beginning To See The Light;
In The Still Of The Night; Just One Of Those Things;
Lullaby Of Birdland; Night Flight; Oh, Lady, Be Good;
Opus One; Perdido; Petite Fleur; Satin Doll; So Nice;
Splanky; Straight No Chaser; That Old Black Magic;
Waltz For Debbie; Wave and Who's Sorry Now?

Order No. AM952435

The Real Book of **Blues**

225 big blues numbers including...
After You've Gone; All Or Nothing At All; Black Coffee;
Blues Stay Away From Me; Bluesette; Body And Soul;
Chelsea Bridge; Crazy Man Blues; Dust My Broom;
Fever; Frankie And Johnny; Georgia On My Mind;
Here's That Rainy Day; How Insensitive; If I Had You;
Lazybones; Li'l Darlin'; Memphis Blues; Misty; Moonglow;
More Than You Know; Singing The Blues; Solitude; Sunny;
When Sunny Gets Blue and Worried Man Blues.

Order No. AM952446

The Real Book of **Great Songs**

Over 200 all-time great songs including...
A Fine Romance; A Woman In Love; Amapola; Arrivederci Roma;
Be Mine Tonight; Carolina Moon; Climb Ev'ry Mountain;
Delicado; Fools Rush In; For All We Know; Getting To Know You;
I Left My Heart In San Francisco; My Favourite Things;
Oklahoma; Paper Roses; Raindrops Keep Falling On My Head;
She; Spanish Eyes; Strangers In The Night; The Folks Who Live
On The Hill; The Twelfth Of Never; This Guy's In Love With You;
Tonight; Too Young; Unchained Melody; Unforgettable;
What Kind Of Fool Am I and Yesterday When I Was Young.

Order No. AM952468

The Real Book of **Favourite Classics**

Famous classical themes from over 60 great composers including...
Rule Britannia (Arne); Air On The 'G' String (J.S. Bach);
Ode To Joy (Beethoven); Themes from 'Carmen' (Bizet);
Hungarian Dances Nos. 4, 5 & 6 (Brahms); España (Chabrier);
Prelude Op.28 No.20 (Chopin); Trumpet Voluntary (Clarke);
Clair De Lune (Debussy); Nimrod (Elgar); Largo (Handel);
Chorale St. Anthony (Haydn); Liebestraum No.3 (Liszt);
Themes from Eine Kleine Nachtmusik (Mozart);
Ave Maria (Schubert); Radetzky March (J. Strauss);
Theme from Piano Concerto No.1 (Tchaikovsky) and
Themes from 'The Four Seasons' (Vivaldi).

Order No. AM952479

www.musicsales.com

All these superb music books are available from good music
retailers, or, in case of difficulty, contact: Music Sales Limited,
Newmarket Road, Bury St. Edmunds, Suffolk IP33 3YB.
Telephone 01284 725725; Fax 01284 702592.

for all keyboards...
Check out these great songbooks!

Your favourite music arranged for all keyboards complete with chord symbols and lyrics.

**Big Band Classics
For All Keyboards**
Thirty-five of the best big band hits, including In The Mood, Night Train, Perdido, Satin Doll, Splanky, Take The 'A' Train and That Old Black Magic. Complete with suggested registrations and rhythms. 96pp.
Order No. AM87582

**Classical Themes
For All Keyboards**
A collection of 50 popular classical pieces from the world's top composers skilfully arranged by Daniel Scott. 8opp.
Order No. AM85317

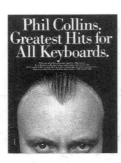

**Phil Collins:
Greatest Hits
For All Keyboards**
Thirty-six of his best songs including Against All Odds (Take A Look At Me Now), All Of My Life, Another Day In Paradise, Colours, Sussudio and You Can't Hurry Love. 118pp.
Order No. AM80664

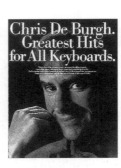

**Chris De Burgh:
Greatest Hits
For All Keyboards**
Thirty-five of his greatest songs, including Borderline, Missing You, Tender Hands and The Lady In Red. 136pp.
Order No. AM81837

**The Doors
For All Keyboards**
A great collection of classic hits. Includes Hello, I Love You, Light My Fire, Riders On The Storm, Strange Days and Waiting For The Sun. 96pp.
Order No. AM928268

**Favourite
TV Themes
For All Keyboards**
Includes Coronation Street, Dad's Army, EastEnders, Last Of The Summer Wine, Miami Vice and Steptoe And Son. 8opp.
Order No. AM957209

**Jazz & Blues
For All Keyboards**
Fifty great jazz and blues standards. Includes Ain't Misbehavin', Georgia On My Mind, I'm Getting Sentimental Over You, That Ole Devil Called Love, Tuxedo Junction and The Lady Sings The Blues. 144pp.
Order No. AM85291

**Elton John
For All Keyboards**
Twenty-five hit songs, including Candle In The Wind, Daniel, Goodbye Yellowbrick Road, Rocket Man and Your Song. 96pp.
Order No. AM89526

**Nursery Rhymes
For All Keyboards**
Fifty children's favourites including Lavender Blue, Sing A Song Of Sixpence, The Grand Old Duke Of York and Three Blind Mice. 96pp.
Order No. AM90033

**250 All-Time Hits
Book 4**
A mega collection of songs for all keyboard players. Includes Can't Buy Me Love, Heartbreaker, Lucille Oh, Pretty Woman, The Way You Look Tonight and Under The Boardwalk . 184pp.
Order No. AM91020

All these superb music books, and many more, are available from good music retailers, or in case of difficulty contact:
Music Sales Limited, Newmarket Road, Bury St. Edmunds, Suffolk IP33 3YB.
Telephone 01284 725725; Fax 01284 702592.

www.musicsales.com